For Kate and Fred

This edition is
published and distributed
exclusively by
DISCOVERY TOYS
Martinez, CA

First published in 1988
in Great Britain by
Walker Books Ltd., London

© 1988 Martin Baynton

Printed in Italy

ISBN 0-939979-25-X

JANE and the DRAGON

Martin Baynton

DISCOVERY TOYS

Jane hated sewing. Every morning she sat with her mother practicing her stitches, and every morning she gazed down at the knights practicing their swordplay in the courtyard below.

Jane longed to be a knight. Nothing else would do, and she told her mother so.

Her mother laughed.

"Such foolishness," she said. "You will be a lady-in-waiting. Perhaps, like me, you will become lady-in-waiting to the Queen herself."

Jane was very upset. But she was determined to be a knight and she went to tell her father.

Her father laughed.

"What nonsense," he said. "Only boys can become knights."

Jane told the King.
The King laughed.
"Of course, of course,"
he said. But he hadn't
really heard her, for
the King listened to
no one but himself.

Jane told the Prince, the King's only son.
The Prince said nothing. He just
laughed and pushed her over
in the royal sandpit.

Jane told the knights themselves. They laughed and dressed her in fine armor that was too big for her and set her on a straw horse.

They thought it was great fun until they saw tears trickle out from under the helmet. The knights were sorry. They had not meant to be unkind.

Finally Jane told the court jester. The jester didn't laugh. Of all the people Jane had spoken to, he alone listened and understood.

He took Jane to his room and opened a wooden chest. Inside was a small suit of armor.

"I wanted to be a knight as well," said the jester, "but I was too small. This armor is my secret; I put it on sometimes . . . and dream a little. I want you to have it."

Jane was overjoyed.

"But what about your dream?" she asked.

"I was never really brave enough," he said. "You dream it for me."

From that day on, Jane's sewing got worse. She was too busy watching the knights – watching and learning.
    And whenever the knights were out chasing the King's enemies, Jane would go to their quarters, put on her armor and practice.

She practiced her swordplay.

She practiced her horseplay.

She even practiced
her victory speeches.

Then one terrible day, an enormous green dragon came and stole the Prince.

The King and Queen were horrified. They called for the knights, but the knights were away at a jousting carnival.

"Is there no one left who can save our son?" cried the King.

They were very surprised when a small knight ran into the courtyard, saddled up the Prince's pony and galloped away after the dragon.

Jane followed the dragon to his mountain lair.

"Release the boy!" she demanded in her sternest voice.

The dragon laughed.

"Make me!" he roared, and his hot breath singed the plume on Jane's helmet.

Jane laughed and took off her helmet. The dragon was amazed.

"You're just a girl, I could fry you for breakfast."

"Yes, that would be easy for you. It would be easy for me to be a lady-in-waiting, people expect it. But I want to be a knight. What do you want?"

"I want to be loved," sobbed the dragon, and he covered his face with a spiky brown wing.

Jane put down her sword and kissed him. "I love you," she said.

"Oh, thank you, thank you," said the dragon, and he sobbed all the louder.

"Now I have to take the Prince home," said Jane. "The King and Queen will be dreadfully worried."

"Will you visit me sometimes?" asked the dragon.

"Every Saturday," Jane promised. "But now we really must go."

And she gave the dragon a hug and another kiss.

It was late in the day when they arrived back at the castle. The entire court rushed out to greet them. The King and Queen were overjoyed to see their son – but who was the mysterious knight?

Jane took off her helmet, and the crowd gasped.

Her father just stood there with his mouth wide open. Her mother fainted gracefully.

"Dear Jane," said the King, "how can we ever thank you?"

"Your Majesty, I would like to become a proper knight please, with every Saturday off to visit a friend."

"Certainly, certainly," said the King, and he called for the royal scribe, who wrote the contract out there and then.

That evening the King gave a royal ball. Everyone was there, including Jane's mother and father, who had recovered from their shock and were now very proud of their fearless daughter.

Jane was the guest of honor.

"You must choose a partner, Jane," said the King, "and lead the dancing."

All the handsome young men waited, each one hoping to be chosen.

But Jane took the jester's hand and led him onto the floor.

"Thank you for the armor," said Jane.

"Thank you for the dream," said the jester.

And together they danced and danced and danced.